D0305593

L.O.L. SURPRISE!™

Special 2023 Edition

LittleBrother
BOOKS

Published 2022. Little Brother Books Ltd, Ground Floor,
23 Southernhay East, Exeter, Devon, EX1 1QL
Printed in China. Xuantan Temple Industrial Zone, Gulao Town, Heshan, Guangdong.
books@littlebrotherbooks.co.uk | www.littlebrotherbooks.co.uk

The Little Brother Books trademark, email and website addresses, are the sole and exclusive
properties of Little Brother Books Limited. Images used under license from Shutterstock.

MGA

lolsurprise.com | mgae.com

© MGA Entertainment, Inc.
L.O.L. SURPRISE!™ is a trademark of MGA
in the U.S. and other countries. All logos, names,
characters, likenesses, images, slogans, and
packaging appearance are the property of MGA.
Used under license by Little Brother Books Ltd.

© MGA

© MGA

You're a QUEEN

Hey queen, great to meet you! Are you ready for some total L.O.L. fun? See how u rule at school, read a super story and be prepared to get ur puzzle on. Your best B.B.s are waiting, so let's go!

Use your best pens to add the finishing touches to the B.B.'s outfits.

Kitty Queen

Queen Bee

© MGA

Cosmic Queen

Bling Queen

Diva

Boss Queen

Turn the page for more L.O.L. fun!

7

© MGA

The next smash-hit L.O.L. club.
Starring... you!

Your club, your rules, your way.

How's your L.O.L. collection going? Does it need a little **extra** something? Give it a **ba-boom boost** with your very own club... with you as the main attraction.

This is what I look like as an L.O.L.

Draw an L.O.L. self portrait here.

What's in a name?

The next level girls are here to help you channel your inner L.O.L. First up, you need a snappy name for your club. Call it something related to a hobby, or make up something funny, like Oh so sassy girls!

My club is called...

My name's:

© MGA

And here are all my friends.

Our club is all about…

We stand for:

1..
2..
3..
4..
5..

Our rules are...

1
2
3
4
5

You'll find us @

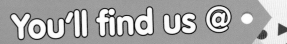

Write your favourite places, here.

© MGA

9

Candy Jumble!

Puzzles don't get sweeter than this!

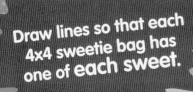

Draw lines so that each 4x4 sweetie bag has one of each sweet.

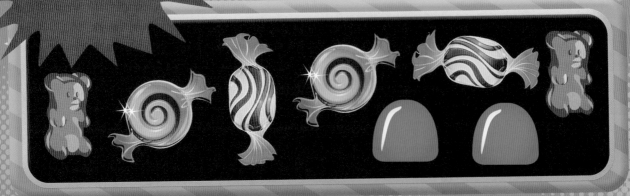

ANSWERS O p76-77!

© MGA

GO 4 GOAL

Kicks is an expert on the ball.

Use a pencil to help **Kicks dribble the ball** through the maze to the **goal**.

START!

FINISH!

ANSWERS ON p76-77!

11

© MGA

Having a BALL!

These queens are born red-carpet ready!

Can you **spot** the six differences between the two pictures?

Colour in a crown each time you spot a difference.

SEE ME IN A CROWN

Draw a line to put the next crown into the pattern.

A B
C D

YASS!

Can you give Charm Queen's outfit a colourful makeover?

ANSWERS ON p76-77!

13

© MGA

Yass, School QUEEN!

So you rule school, right? But what's your queen style?

Circle one answer for each question.

UH-OH! SCHOOL DRAMA! HOW DO YOU SORT IT?

- Step in and tell everyone how it is
- Listen to all sides then find common ground
- Steer well clear

WHAT KIND OF SCHOOL EVENT WOULD YOU ORGANISE?

- School sleepover
- Onesie day
- Cake sale for charity

WHAT'S YOUR KIND OF AFTER SCHOOL CLUB?

- Drama
- Netball
- Music

© MGA

FRIENDSHIP STYLE?

- Lots and lots
- A few solid favourites
- One or two brilliant besties

AT SCHOOL, YOU'D BE:

- Organising games
- Chatting with friends
- Reading up on cool stuff

ADD UP YOUR ANSWERS TO REVEAL HOW U RULE SCHOOL!

MOSTLY BLUE CROWNS
YOU'RE MERBABY

You're a true school queen Snap your fingers, and it magically gets done! Everyone loves to please you, just be sure to help others, too.

MOSTLY PINK CROWNS
YOU'RE PRECIOUS

You're a great leader, but you love to make sure everyone in the land is happy, too! You don't mind not being centre stage if it makes other people smile!

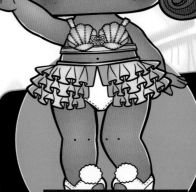

MOSTLY GREEN CROWNS
YOU'RE TREASURE

You're more of a quiet leader - you like to observe those around you then work out your next move. But once you know your plan, it's all systems go.

15

© MGA

Mini B.B. scene

Make a perfectly petite pop-up party!

INSTRUCTIONS
- Carefully detach the facing page, making sure you've finished with the other side first.
- Fold along the dotted line so that the mini scene stands up.
- Carefully cut out the L.O.L. dolls, then fold the tabs over so that the dolls stand up. You're now ready for a pop-up party!

SAFETY
Get a grown-up to help you when using scissors.

YOU'LL NEED
Scissors

If you don't want to cut up your book, photocopy or scan and print page 17 instead.

© MGA

Fold

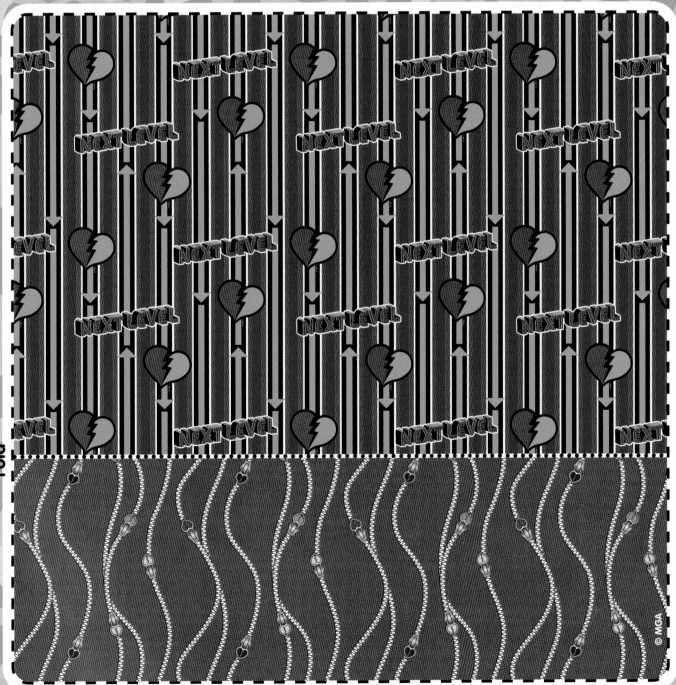

Fold

© MGA

DOODLE A UNIQUELY U L.O.L.

Put your sketching skills to the test, and see what they say about you!

Here's your chance to be the **artist** you've always dreamed of!
Here's what to do. **Doodle** a totally fabulous L.O.L. doll. Once you've finished, close your eyes for 5 seconds. Open them, then pick the L.O.L. on the opposite page you're most drawn to. Then see what it reveals about your doodle!

Yang

Yin

Tough Guy

If you picked Tough Guy...
You know your own mind and hate being told what to do. You're totally independent and that's just the way you like it!

If you picked Yin...
You're a daydreaming type that likes to live inside your imagination. The sky's the limit as far as you're concerned!

If you picked Yang...
You're a bundle of energy, always ready for the next adventure. You love to try new things, and no challenge is too much for you.

© MGA

VACAY day!

The L.O.L.s love summer! Can you find all the beachy words in the gird?

```
S U A H O L I D A Y
U U C Z O Y B Z B Y
F A N H B V U R U L
P L S G I I I D R S
A J I X L L K K A R
R B E P Y A L I Y V
T E T T F Y S Z N I
Y A L V S L J S G I
N C I L B E O A E V
I H L C M T T P L S
```

TICK THESE WORDS OFF AS YOU FIND THEM.

Holiday ☐ Sunglasses ☐

Jetset ☐ Chill ☐

Flip flop ☐ Party ☐

Bikini ☐ Beach ☐

ANSWERS ON p76-77!

© MGA

THAT'S SNOW BUSINESS

Time to ch...
with the bes...
winter B.B.s!

NO TWO SNOWFLAKES ARE THE SAME, AND NEITHER ARE B.B. FRIEND
FORMATIONS! CAN YOU SPOT THIS PATTERN IN THE GRID?

© MGA

FIERCE FEET

When a party invite turns up that's just so hot, Boss Queen just has to go!

"OMG!" shrieked Boss Queen, leaping around the room. "You totally won't believe what's just arrived through the letterbox. It's an invitation to the L.O.L. annual fierce-athon!." Boss Queen had never been so happy. Finally, she had made the A-grade cut!

Diva and M.C. Swag watched Boss Queen leap and shriek, and jump and pose."We'd better watch out for our girl," Diva whispered to M.C. Swag. "She is waaaaaayyy too excited about this!" Just then, Boss Queen tripped over her stacked sparkly shoes and tumbled to the floor. "Oh no! My leg has swollen up. How will I make it to the the fierce-athon now? My life is totally oh-vah!"

M.C. Swag looked on at Boss Queen. "We gotta help her, Diva! What can we do?" Diva thought for a second. "On it!" she chuckled. "I know exactly what to do. Boss Queen, hold it right there, M.C. Swag, you come with me!"

Diva and M.C. Swag grabbed Boss Queen's best clothes, and a few extras. "Right, we are going to style you up to the be the fiercest of the fierce, swollen leg or not!" The friends started to bandage up Boss Queen's leg, with of course, a sparkly bandage, then they handed her a pair of bejewelled customised crutches and matching sunglasses.

© MGA

"When life trips you up, you've got to style it it out!" laughed M.C. Swag. "You can do this, you look totes amaze!" Boss Queen thought for a moment. "You know what, with my two best pals beh... me, I can style anything out. I'm going to be the fier... that ever hobbled the red carpet!"

Later that nig... her stuff so hard, she won the award for the... she dedicated her award to? "This... u and M.C. Swag" ...girls!"

Re... gether, slay together. ...st, every time!

ANSWERS ON p76-77!

© MGA

Make a L.O.L. Pencil Topper

Next level stationery coming right up!

INSTRUCTION

- Carefully cut out all the pencil toppers.
- Wrap the blue band around the top of your pencil.
- Secure the band to the pencil with sticky tape.
- Your pencil topper is ready!

YOU'LL NEED
- Scissors
- Pencils
- Sticky tape

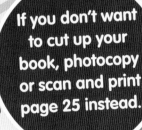

If you don't want to cut up your book, photocopy or scan and print page 25 instead.

SAFETY
Get a grown-up to help you when using scissors.

© MGA

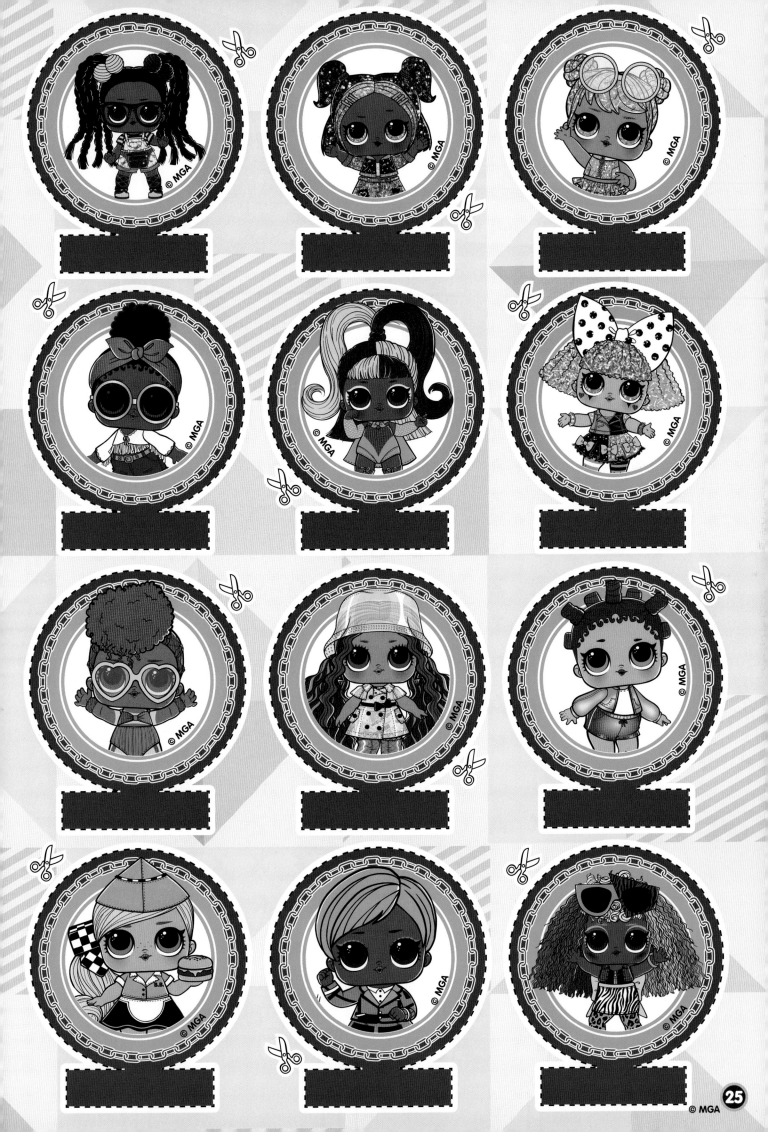

TOTALLY AMAZING AND AWESOME!

Make every day a yay day!

CAN YOU FIND ALL THE WORDS IN THE GRID? USE A PENCIL
TO SCORE THEM OUT EACH TIME YOU SPOT ONE.

```
F D E G H Z W E L E A E Q I N
N E A I V L S T A R V F S R D
J Z V Q A B H N F I E R C E N
U P K O S H S S X F N X N L W
C D A S N R E U B V H E W R G
Y O N R Z X N R L Q S I T L L
C J Y K T E S P I Z P X Q O I
H V O J B Y A R C U A R N H T
T H O O R A Y T I K D W F W L T
K A O O K H I S V X I B O V E
E A U J U T O E C U K L W K R
N R Y X A O N F E W Z F M K A
D H I M R E V D T F X X H A L
X A F L Z B X K Y I R Y L O L
Y C I J O T O M Y S R L F X Y
```

709

TICK THESE
WORDS OFF
AS YOU FIND
THEM.

Glitterally ☐   **Surprise** ☐   **Fierce** ☐   **Hooray** ☐

Sensation ☐   **Wow** ☐   **Party** ☐   **Star** ☐

ANSWERS ON
P76-77!

 © MGA

Extra Sweet!

Bring Sugar Queen's dream to life with your brightest colours.

Colour each sweetie a different colour!

© MGA

MEET...
Pranksta

Taking her place in the spotlight!

Pranksta's catch phrase: **Made ya bling!**

Pranksta is part of the **theatre club.**

Pranksta loves **pastels**. Pinks, purples and blues are her favourite hues.

Pranksta loves to **perform** and is always first to take a turn in the **spotligh**t.

© MGA

Designer RULEZ

Kitty Queen is going to the ball! Design her a royally regal outfit.

© MGA

Her highness RULEZ!

Get puzzling like the queen you are!

1

Boss queen is on her way to werk! Which path should she take to reach Charm Queen?

A

B

C

2

Can you spot the 5 crowns hidden on the page?

© MGA

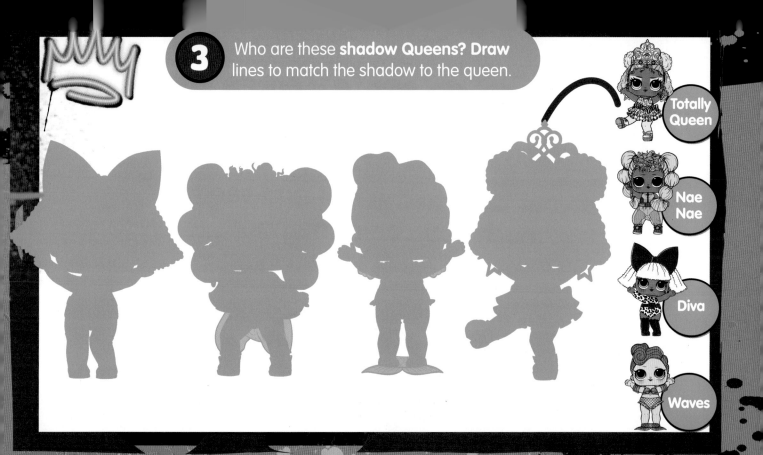

3 Who are these **shadow Queens?** Draw lines to match the shadow to the queen.

Totally Queen

Nae Nae

Diva

Waves

4 Which piece fits back into the picture?

L.O.L. SURPRISE!

I'M A QUEEN

BABY

MISS PUNK

A

B

C

ANSWERS ON P76-77!

31

©MGA

Memory magic

Put your skills to the test and see how much you can remember!

B.B. NATION

 ## INSTRUCTIONS

Cover up the right hand side of the page.

Study the picture on this page for 20 seconds.

Then cover up the left hand side of the page, and look at the right hand side.

See how many questions you got right!

© MGA

B.B. NATION

1

There were 4 BBs in the original picture.

☒ ☑

2

M.C. Swag has a number on her top in the original picture.

☒ ☑

3

Diva's boots are pink in the original picture.

☒ ☑

4

Neon Q.T. has a blue stripe in her hair in the original picture.

☒ ☑

5

Queen Bee's eyes are green in the original picture.

☒ ☑

ANSWERS ON p76–77!

HOW MANY DID YOU GET RIGHT?

1 OR LESS

Hmmm, maybe you need to look a little closer!

2-3

You're taking it all in, but you're not a details person.

4 OR MORE

Wow, you're a memory magician, well done!

© MGA

Keepin' it SWEET

The L.O.L.s are packed with flavour!

Can you spot the odd one out on each row?

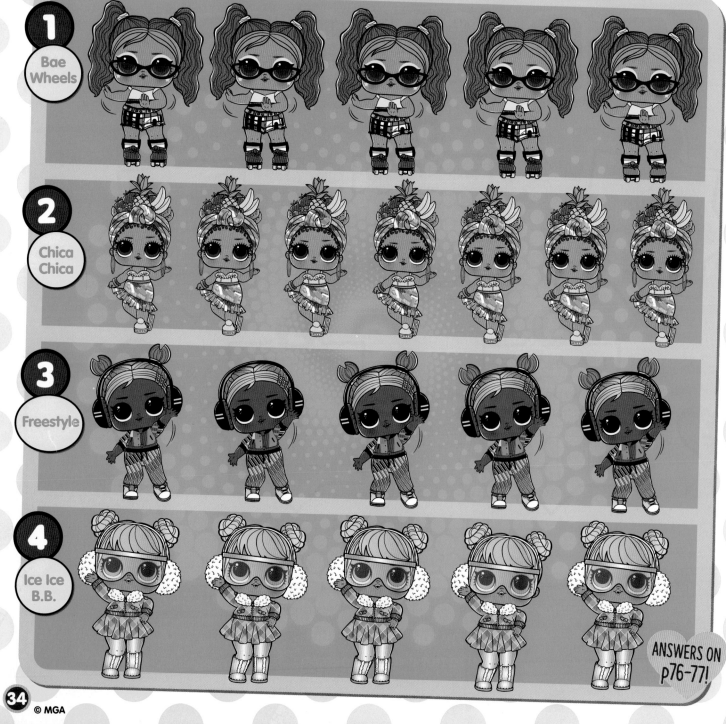

1 Bae Wheels

2 Chica Chica

3 Freestyle

4 Ice Ice B.B.

ANSWERS ON p76-77!

34 © MGA

IN DA BAG

Test your memory skills.

SURFER BABE HAS LEFT HER BAG AT THE BEACH. STUDY THE CONTENTS, THEN TURN THE PAGE TO PLAY A COOL MEMORY GAME!

NOW TURN THE PAGE TO PLAY THE BEACH BAG GAME!

© MGA

IN DA BAG ...CONTINUED!

Time to put your memory skills to the test.

DID YOU TAKE THE CHALLENGE ON THE PREVIOUS PAGE? GREAT! LET'S SEE HOW MUCH YOU CAN REMEMBER!

TICK ALL OF THE ITEMS THAT WERE IN THE BAG.

Sunglasses

Notebook

Book

Purse

Lipstick

Phone

Perfume

Lip balm

ANSWERS ON p76-77!

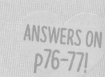

© MGA

RA RA WRONG?

Honey Bun has an eye for fine detail!

Honey Bun is looking for her perfect match! Which picture is the only one that matches this one?

A

B

C

D

E

GOOO TEAM!

ANSWERS ON p76-77!

37

© MGA

MEET... FOXY

B.B.'s don't come better than this!

Name: Foxy
Club: Retro
Rarity: Fabulous

Foxy loves to wear a **vintage scarf** in her hair.

Foxy's older sister is **Sunset**, and her little brother is **Lil Foxy**.

Foxy's catchphrase: **Outta sight, BB!**

Foxy is part of the **retro club.**

Foxy is all about the **bohemian vibes!**

© MGA

WHAT'S YOUR Royal NAME?

Lets find out, your highness!

Pick one name from the first list, one from the second. Put 'em together and voila! Your royal name is ready!

Royal

The greatest

Highness

Princess

Esteemed

Everlived

Royally

Upon high

Never beaten

My royal name is

_____

© MGA

PUZZLE PARADE

These totally awesome divas are loud and proud!

WAKE UP

Sleepy Bones needs to wake up. Help her to sleepwalk to Go-Go Gurl so they can get their day started!

START

HELLO, MISS!

Which Miss Baby is the odd one out?

A   B   C   D

FINISH

IT GURL

Draw the sunglasses on It Baby and colour them in black.

ANSWERS ON p76-77!

© MGA

HOW SWEET ARE YOU?

Answer what you love most to discover just what makes you as cute as candy!

I LOVE WEARING:
- **A** An outfit bought by my mum
- **B** A customised t-shirt
- **C** A friendship bracelet

I LOVE HAVING:
- **A** Bike ride
- **B** Sleepovers
- **C** TV nights

I TOTALLY LOVE MY:
- **A** Mum
- **B** Pets
- **C** BFFs

I LOVE SMELLING:
- **A** Flowers
- **B** Perfume
- **C** Cookies

I LOVE MY FRIENDS COS:
- **A** They're super-stylish
- **B** They're funny
- **C** They're down-to-earth

HOW DID YOU GET ON?

MOSTLY A

YOU'RE MISS BABY

You and Miss Baby are totally sweet things, and you love chilling out and joking around with your family.

MOSTLY B

YOU'RE SUGAR

Just like Sugar, you're sweet and sassy. All the little things you do really make a big difference.

MOSTLY C

YOU'RE SUPA STAR

Well hello, Candy Queen. Being a caring B.B. like Supa Star means you have loads of best friends.

© MGA

We're all QUEENS

It's time to think like a royal B.B. and fill in this page!

MY NAME IS
QUEEN
....

DOODLE A CROWN YOU'D LOVE TO WEAR HERE.

THESE WOULD BE MY LADIES IN WAITING – AKA TRUSTED INNER CIRCLE.

1..

2..

3..

WHAT WOULD BE THE BEST THING ABOUT BEING A QUEEN?

☑ The jewels

☑ Being in charge

☑ Meeting lots of people

☑ Living in a palace

© MGA

IF I WAS QUEEN, I
WOULD MAKE THESE
THINGS LAW:

1..
....
2..
....
3..
....

DESIGN SOME ROYAL-NAIL
ART HERE.

DESCRIBE YOUR
QUEEN STYLE IN
THREE WORDS.

1   **2**   **3**

WOULD YOU MAKE EVERYONE
BOW EVERY TIME YOU WALKED
IN A ROOM? CIRCLE ONE.

Yes

No

IF I WAS QUEEN, MY SLOGAN
WOULD BE:

☑ Royal Realness

☑ **Queen of Everything**

☑ Sassy Queen

☑ **#Queening**

© MGA

STRUT UR STUFF!

DRAW A CATWALK READY OUTFIT FOR FIERCE.

© MGA

SPORT MUDDLE

MATCH THE WORD HALVES TO FIND SEVEN TYPES OF SPORTS THAT THE ALL-STAR B.B.'S JUST LOVE PLAYING.

foot

swim

ice

hoc

run

skateboard

yo

ten

ga

skating

ball

ning

nis

ing

ming

key

ANSWERS ON p76-77!

45

© MGA

SECRET NUMBER

Find out your special number to discover who your L.O.L. Surprise! BFF is.

1. Using the chart below, add up the number value of the letters of your first and last name.

2. If your sum has two or more digits for example, 27 - add those numbers together 2 + 7 = 9

3. You may need to do this again to get a single digit.

4. The final one-digit figure is your secret L.O.L. Surprise! number.

A = 1   H = 8   O = 15   V = 22
B = 2   I = 9   P = 16   W = 23
C = 3   J = 10   Q = 17   X = 24
D = 4   K = 11   R = 18   Y = 25
E = 5   L = 12   S = 19   Z = 26
F = 6   M = 13   T = 20
G = 7   N = 14   U = 21

MY SECRET NUMBER IS

© MGA

WHAT YOUR SECRET NUMBER MEANS

1

YOUR BFF IS V.R.Q.T.

You're great with coming up with new ideas, and getting others to go along with them. Life with you two would be a lot of fun.

2

YOUR BFF IS BEATS

You and Beats love nothing better than making people have fun. Your entertaining skills are legendary!

3

YOUR BFF IS ROYAL HIGH-NEY

You and Royal High-Ney don't see any reason why the world shouldn't be kinder, greener and more fun. We totally hear you.

4

YOUR BFF IS DANCE BOT

You and Dance Bot love music, moves and all things dancing. We'd love to hang out with the pair of you.

5

YOUR BFF IS STARDUST QUEEN

You and Stardust Queen would be amazing together. You're both royally good fun and love the spotlight.

6

YOUR BFFS IS SOUL BABE

You value love and BFF above everything else. You would have so much fun gathering your friends and family together.

7

YOUR BFF IS GLAMSTRONAUT

You and Glamstronaut would have loads of fun creating epic adventures together. Please invite us!

8

YOUR BFF IS JELLY JAM

You and Jelly Jam are a match made in heaven. Others look up to you and love your can-do attitude and oh-so-sweet nature.

9

YOUR BFF IS PRANKSTA

You love having fun, just like Pranksta. You're super-creative, and love standing out from the crowd. You go, girl!

© MGA

MEET... Spice

This Sweet Tooth B.B. is extra-spicy

Don't be fooled by the horns, Spice is one of the **friendliest** B.B.s in town.

Spice always brings **extra flavour**. She may be **sassy**, but she's **extra sweet**.

Spice's catchphrase: **Hot like a pepper!**

This doll always adds **extra flavour to her outfits** whether it's by adding **stripy tights** or her **pink DMs**.

Spice is part of the **opposites club.**

 © MGA

LET'S PARTY

It's Astro B.B.'s birthday. Which line leads to her pile of presents?

A
B
C
D
E

ANSWERS ON p76-77!

© MGA

SO AWESOME!

These B.B.s are totally rad when it comes to feeling good!

1 PUT ON A HAPPY FACE

The Totally Awesome crew know that a smile has a feel-good ripple effect. Your brain gets an instant boost from the muscles you use around the eyes and lips, plus you'll feel even better as people can't help but smile back at you. Grin and let the world grin with you.

2 SAY THANK YOU

Next time you get a compliment, make like these B.B.s, smile and say, 'Thank you!'. You - and the person who complimented you - will instantly feel good. And you'll both want to give and receive compliments more often. Hurrah!

3 WEAR COLOUR

We're not talking head-to-toe neon orange here, (unless you want to), but the B.B.s know that a pop of colour like a bright bag or t-shirt can instantly lighten your mood, and make you feel amazing. Go on, give it a go!

©MGA

4 CHOOSE FRIENDS WISELY

Who we hang with has a big effect on us. Spend time around people who feel good about themselves and want you to feel good about yourself, just like the Totally Awesome gang. Don't forget to tell your BFFs exactly why they rock.

5 KNOW YOU'RE GREAT

All the Totally Awesome B.B.'s have a great attitude, and know exactly what they like about themselves. They choose to look at what's great about themselves, rather than what's bad. Remind yourself every day, just why you're great.

WRITE 5 THINGS THAT MAKE YOU FEEL INSTANTLY AWESOME HERE!

1...

2...

3...

4...

5...

© MGA

What's your DREAM JOB?

Answer Boss Queen's questions to find your perfect career fit!

You have a long homework project to finish. You:

A Put it off til the last minute

B Get someone to help you

C Finish it early

Your idea holiday would be:

A Hiking in the mountains

B Sailing round the world

C Exploring a famous city

It's sports day at school. You:

A Enter lots of events

B Organise everyone else

C Help writing down the scores

It's your birthday treat. You want to:

A Go on a day-trip somewhere totally new

B Go out for a pizza with your pals

C Head to the cinema and watch a movie

If you were to write a book, it would be about:

A A famous explorer

B Wild animals

C Anything. You just love writing

Which outfit is more you?

A Jeans and t-shirt

B A cute dress

C Leggings and a cosy sweatshirt

HOW DID YOU DO?

 MOSTLY A ADVENTURE GAL

You're adventurous and dream of travelling. You'd be a brilliant **TV reporter** or **pilot**.

 **MOSTLY B KIND-HEARTED PAL**

You're good with people and animals. You'd make a fabulous **vet** or **doctor**.

 MOSTLY C BOOK WORM

You love books and magazines. You could be a **writer, designer,** an **artist** or **work in a museum**.

© MGA

What to do: Pick the card you feel most drawn to. Then turn over to read your destiny. Ooh!

© MGA

A class trip will give you ample time to bond with a new friend.

Listen to your BFFs, they have your best interests at heart.

It's time for your close-up. Try out for the school play.

A group project will be more fun than you ever imagined.

Spend time with your family. You'll be so pleased you did.

Don't be shy when a new girl chats to you. They'll be an ace part of your crew.

A new club is calling your name. You'll meet some forever friends there.

Take a moment, slow down and get back that creativity.

Quick thinking will always get you back on track.

© MGA

CHILL OUT

Get warmed up by finding the word 'winter' four times in the grid below, then design a cosy winter outfit.

Look **up, down** and **diagonally**!

E	W	O	X	T	C	W	V	E	R
E	J	I	X	Q	F	S	R	E	L
N	L	P	N	G	S	B	H	Q	D
R	B	K	B	T	E	X	D	N	W
G	H	M	R	K	E	H	B	W	I
X	N	K	G	E	I	R	V	I	N
W	I	N	T	E	R	J	P	N	T
Q	L	A	M	Z	L	P	M	T	E
T	H	X	M	U	J	S	Z	E	R
B	T	D	S	Y	X	T	B	R	E

ANSWERS ON p76-77!

Draw your cosy outfit here!

55

© MGA

JET SET Life!

Wrap your head around these puzzles with the Born 2 Travel gang.

SECRET MESSAGE

Use the key to work out the postcard message that Jet Set Q.T. has received.

JET SET Q.T'S POSTCARD

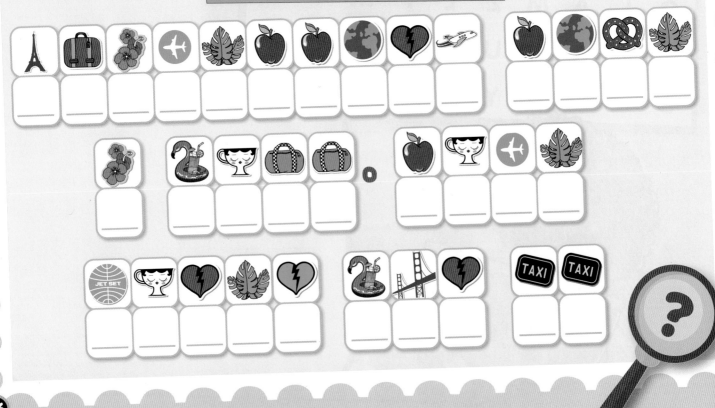

What would you wear on vacay with
Honey Bun? Draw it here.

TRAVEL LIST

What places would
you like to visit.
Write them here.

....
....
....
....
....
....
....
....

SHADOW TIME

Which shadow
exactly matches
Go-Go Gurl's
suitcases?

A

B

C

?

ANSWERS ON
p76-77!

57

© MGA

MEET...
OffBeat

This B.B. is always fierce and outrageously glam!

OffBeat is always reaching for new heights in her **sky-high platform kicks**!

This girl loves to show off her **unique fashion sense**. **Mis-matched hair bobbles** are her signature look!

Offbeat knows how to werk accessories from **cute bum bags** to **fierce animal-print glasses**.

Offbeat's catchphrase: **Good vibes only!**

© MGA

Dance dice BOOGIE

Rule the dance floor with Charm Queen's fierce game!

WHAT TO DO

1. Carefully cut out the dice along the dotted lines.
2. Fold the dice together and glue the tabs in place.
3. Throw the dice and follow the move it lands on.
4. Keep throwing the dice to put together your own unique dance routine.

YOU WILL NEED

- Glue
- Safety scissors

Glue

1
Throw your hands in the air

2
Freestyle

Glue

Glue

Glue

4
Go low

© MGA

6
Kick your legs in the air

3
Shimmy from side to side

Glue

Glue

Glue

If you don't want to cut up your book, photocopy or scan and print page 59 instead.

5
Jump to the beat

SAFETY
Get a grown-up to help you when using scissors.

Glue

© MGA

RU NEXT LEVEL?

Discovering your personality is as easy as 1, 2, 3...!

The first 3 L.O.L. catchphrases you see in the grid will describe you inside out!

```
T O T A L L Y E X T R A 2
B R O U S E D L A C J G F
G L O V I N L I F E C L L
O U T R A G E O U S L A Y
I M D I O G V L U N S M 4
B O S S Q U E E N P O 4 W
R N E X T L E V E L L L O
C B S O O R U R L E C I R
E F I B I H K S I B I F D
Y F N P R A N K S T A E S
A L W A Y S F I E R C E E
```

The words that **describe** my personality are:

1...

2...

3...

Don't agree? Try again!

ANSWERS ON p76-77!

© MGA

SCRUMMY DOODLES

 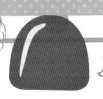 

Design a new sweet for these yummy B.B.s.

It could be...
Chocolate
Gummy pets
Whatever you like.

© MGA

MAKEOVER MADNESS

Give your bedroom a **Totally Awesome** new look!

1 HANG UP YOUR CLOTHES

Or fold 'em away. **Pile up books and games on a shelf** or in a corner. You'll be amazed at how much better it looks!

2 STORE STUFF

Struggling to tidy up? Grab some cardboard boxes or plastic containers and fill them with toys and books you don't use very often. **Stack them in a corner or under the bed.** Simple but oh so effective!

3 CHUCK OUT

Throw away or recycle old things. If any of your belongings are still useful but you don't want them anymore, just give them away. Re-use is the best use!

4 WORK SPACE

Create a corner of your room as a workspace with a small table or desk to lean on. Store paper, pens and books nearby so you can reach them easily. Simples.

© MGA

5 COLOUR SCHEME

Choose your favourite colour, then buy a couple of new accessories such as a silky scarf, cushion or new lampshade to dress up your room. Awesome.

6 THEME IT

Cut out pictures from magazines and use them as posters. You could choose animals or fashion. Frame postcards or buy accessories to match.

7 BRIGHTEN UP

Make your bed every day, then make it look extra bright and comfy with a couple of cushions or a throw-over bedspread.

8 JAZZ UP

Decorate your walls. Hang up a pretty piece of material as a wall-hanger. It doesn't cost much and looks super fabulous.

9 MAKE IT

For a quick decoration, draw your own pictures, tape ribbon to the back, then tie up. You could also make bunting. See page 72.

10 ART ATTACK

Paint a huge mural, buy a cheap clip frame and hang it up. You'll have a piece of art that's totally and utterly unique.

© MGA

B.B. BOUTIQUE

The B.B.s are shopping for new fabulous outfits.

1 There are **10 tricky differences** between picture a and picture b. Can you spot them all?

2 **Colour** in a shopping bag every time you see a difference.

SECRET DIARY

Slumber Queen just wants to have fun with her B.B.s at a sleepover. Fill in her diary for her!

DEAR DIARY

THE B.B.S ARE HEADING OVER FOR A SLEEPOVER TONIGHT, SO IT'S TIME TO GET MY PARTY ON! HERE'S WHAT I'M GOING TO ARRANGE TO MAKE SURE WE DANCE, HAVE FUN AND STAY AWAKE ALL NIGHT. HAPPY DAYS!

SNACKS:...

....

MUSIC:...

....

MOVIES:...

....

GAMES TO PLAY:...

....

HAIRSTYLES TO TRY OUT:...

....

© MGA

Drawing QUEEN

Get your royal rebel doodling skills on, and copy M.C. Queen square by square into the grid below!

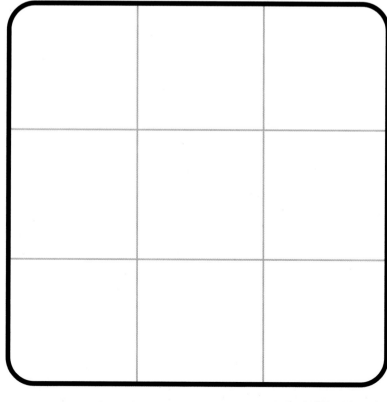

© MGA

Sweet as Candy

Can you **fit all the words** into the grid below? No artificial flavours allowed!

1.
2.
3.
4.
5.
6.
7.
8.

TICK THE WORDS OFF AS YOU FIT 'EM!

- [ ] FLAVOUR
- [ ] SWEET
- [ ] SUGAR
- [ ] SASSY
- [ ] POP
- [ ] CANDY
- [ ] GUMBALLS
- [ ] BON BONS

ANSWERS ON p76-77!

68 © MGA

Hidden message

Find Pink Baby's fierce message especially for you.

Begin at the shaded square at the top.

Trace a path through the letters to spell out words until you reach the second shaded square.

You can go up, down, backwards and forwards, but not diagonally.

R	A	I	N	T	L	O	W	E	A
V	R	I	O	C	I	A	R	W	L
E	S	O	R	S	H	I	N	E	W
T	M	A	B	O	T	T	A	S	E
T	D	H	A	M	I	L	T	O	A
A	Q	P	O	I	T	R	W	Q	L
L	F	O	D	D	A	N	I	O	W
R	A	I	K	K	O	N	E	N	A
Q	W	D	S	Y	K	P	A	X	Y
N	O	R	E	T	T	I	L	G	S

Write the secret message here:

....

....

....

ANSWERS ON p76-77!

69

© MGA

ROYAL PLANNING

Write a story fit for a queen starring Crown Queen.

Write short notes for each section and you'll be surprised at how fast your ideas start to flow.

THE CHARACTERS

Crown Queen is your main character. Now come up with your other characters. What are their names? What are they like?

Scribble your character notes here.

THE SETTING

Think of a time and place for your story. Is it set in your home town or is it in a magical palace far away? Does it take place now, in the past or in the future?

Scribble your setting notes here.

© MGA

THE BEGINNING

Here's where you start to write about Crown Queen and the setting. Think about the mood of your story. Is it funny or sad? Or maybe it's going to be scary. Whooooo!

Write your beginning here.

THE MIDDLE BIT

This is where the plot really gets going. Here's how to do it:

The build up: This is part where you say something more about Crown Queen and something that happens to her. This leads on to the next important bit!

The problem: Something goes wrong or one of your characters has a problem. Is it something silly or something terrible? Is it a mistake or an emergency?

Problem solved: The problem is sorted out somehow and everything turns out OK. Or does it? That's for you to decide.

THE END

Is it a happy ending all around? Did Crown Queen learn something or did the characters change in any way after the experience.

Write your ending here.

Write your middle bit here.

© MGA

BREEZY BUNTING

Make some bunting to decorate your room L.O.L. Surprise! style!

If you don't want to cut up your book, photocopy or scan and print page 73 instead.

YOU WILL NEED

- Old newspaper
- 10 sheets of coloured A4 craft paper
- Stickers or felt-tip pens
- Sticky tape or clothes pegs
- 3 metres of thick string
- Glue
- Safety scissors

SAFETY

Get a grown-up to help you when using scissors.

WHAT TO DO

1. Copy the triangle shape on the opposite page to make a template. Use it to cut out ten flag shapes from your coloured paper.

2. Cut out your dolls and icons around the dashed lines. Use them along with felt-tip pens and stickers to decorate the flags.

3. Starting 20cm in, tape the back of each flag to the length of string, leaving 10cm between each one. Alternatively you could use wooden pegs to attach them to the string.

NOW YOUR BUNTING IS READY. HANG UP AND ENJOY!

Do you rule the SCHOOL?

Find out if you're the queen of study or BFFs.

Start
You study your best on your own

YES → You love curling up with a good book

NO → You're great at school sports

You love curling up with a good book
- YES → You love planning ahead
- NO → You love a good chinwag

You're great at school sports
- YES → You love a good chinwag
- NO → You have loads of BFFS

You love planning ahead
- YES → You love quizzes
- NO → You love quizzes

You love a good chinwag
- YES → You have loads of BFFS
- NO → Getting top marks is so you

You have loads of BFFS
- YES → Friends are the best thing about school
- NO → Getting top marks is so you

You love quizzes
- YES → YOU'RE MATCHY QUEEN
- NO → Getting top marks is so you

Getting top marks is so you
- YES → YOU'RE CHARM QUEEN
- NO → YOU'RE MATCHY QUEEN

Friends are the best thing about school
- YES → YOU'RE CHARM QUEEN
- NO → YOU'RE SELFIE QUEEN

YOU'RE MATCHY QUEEN
You rule when it comes to all things **books**. Your talent at **telling royally good stories** is awesome.

YOU'RE CHARM QUEEN
Wow girl, is there anything you **don't know**? You're **deffo the queen whizz** at any school quiz!

YOU'RE SELFIE QUEEN
Ruling the school is so much more fun **when your BFFS are next to you**. Just make sure you get some work done!

© MGA

GIGGLE FEST

These B.B.s love making each other laugh. Entertain your friends by telling them jokes they've never heard before. Here's how!

WORD SWAP

Some jokes work because a word is replaced by another word that rhymes or sounds similar.

1. Think of a word and then think of a word that could replace it: e.g. donkey, wonky.

2. Think of a question that links the two.

WHAT DO YOU CALL A DONKEY WITH THREE LEGS?

A WONKY!

Try your word swap joke here.

CRAZY COMBINATIONS

Many jokes use objects or activities that sound crazy when linked together.

1. Choose an object and think of two ways to describe it. e.g. A train is fast and long.

2. Think of an activity it could never do e.g. go in a lift.

3. Use this to make up a joke.

WHAT IS LONG AND FAST AND GOES UP AND DOWN?

A TRAIN IN A LIFT!

Try your crazy combinations joke here.

© MGA

Answers

Page 10

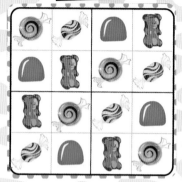

Page 11

Page 12

HAVING A BALL!

SEE ME IN A CROWN

C

Page 20

S	U	A	H	O	L	I	D	A	Y
U	U	C	Z	O	Y	B	Z	B	Y
F	A	N	H	B	V	U	R	U	L
P	L	S	G	I	I	I	D	R	S
A	J	I	X	L	L	K	K	A	R
R	B	E	P	Y	A	L	I	Y	V
T	E	T	T	F	Y	S	Z	N	I
Y	A	L	V	S	L	J	S	G	I
N	C	I	L	B	E	O	A	E	V
I	H	L	C	M	T	T	P	L	S

Page 21

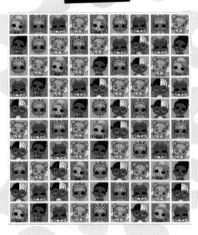

Page 26

TOTALLY AMAZING AND AWESOME!
Make every day a yay day!

Page 30-31

Her highness RULEZ!

Get puzzling like the queen you are!

Page 32-33

MEMORY MAGIC

1 Yes

2 Yes

3 Yes

4 No

5 No

Page 34

Keepin' it Sweet
The L.O.Ls are packed with flavour!

Page 36

IN DA BAG ...CONTINUED!
Time to put your memory skills to the test.

Page 37

RA RA WRONG?
Honey Bun has an eye for fine detail!

© MGA

Page 40 ●

Page 45 ●

HELLO, MISS!

Which Miss Baby is the odd one out?

A   B   C   D

SPORT MUDDLE

football
swimming
ice skating
hockey
skateboarding
yoga
tennis

Page 49 ●

LET'S PARTY

It's Astro B.B.'s birthday. Which line leads to her pile of presents?

Page 55 ●

CHILL OUT

Page 56-57 ●

JET SET Q.T'S POSTCARD

Travelling like a boss.
Love Honey Bun xx

SHADOW TIME

C

Page 60 ●

R U NEXT LEVEL ?

Page 65 ●

Page 68 ●

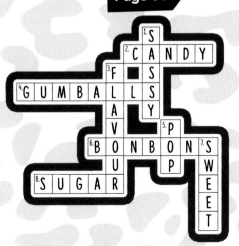

1. S
2. CANDY
3. F
4. GUMBALLS
SASSY
5. P
6. BONBON
7. SWEET
8. SUGAR

Page 69 ●

Hidden message

Find Pink Baby's fierce message especially for you.

Write the secret message here.